English

Key Stage 2
For ages 10-11

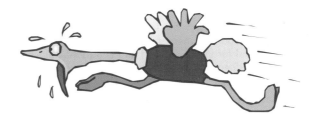

Practise & Learn

Published by CGP

Editors:
Claire Boulter
Rebecca Tate

With thanks to Luke Antieul and
Maxine Petrie for the proofreading.

ISBN: 978 1 84762 734 6

With thanks to Jan Greenway and Laura Jakubowski for the copyright research.

Excerpts from 'Anne of Green Gables' are reproduced here with the authorization of Heirs of
L.M. Montgomery Inc.

'Anne of Green Gables' and other indicia of "Anne" are trademarks and Canadian official marks
of the Anne of Green Gables Licensing Authority Inc.

'L.M. Montgomery' is a trademark of Heirs of L.M. Montgomery Inc.

The extract on page 29 is from 'The Liberators' by Philip Womack © Bloomsbury, 2010.
With thanks to Philip Womack and Bloomsbury for permission to reproduce this extract.

Every effort has been made to locate copyright holders and obtain permission to reproduce sources.
For those sources where it has been difficult to trace the copyright holder of the work, we would
be grateful for information. If any copyright holder would like us to make an amendment to the
acknowledgements, please notify us and we will gladly update the book at the next reprint. Thank you.

Groovy website: www.cgpbooks.co.uk
Printed by Elanders Ltd, Newcastle upon Tyne
Jolly bits of clipart from CorelDRAW®

Based on the classic CGP style created by Richard Parsons.

Contents

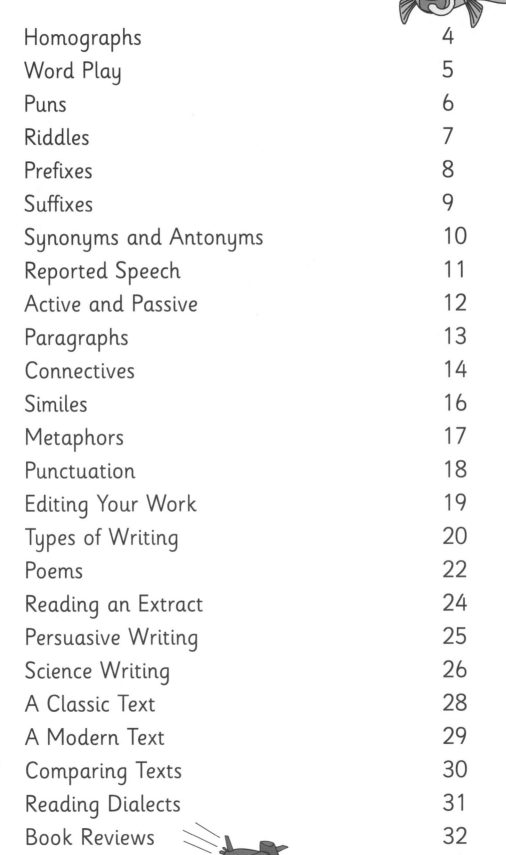

Homographs

Homographs are words that are spelled the same, but have different meanings.

> They had a **row** about who would **row** the boat.

Sometimes they sound the same.

> I want to **row** the blue boat in the second **row**.

Each sentence is missing two homographs that don't sound the same. Match a picture clue to each sentence and write in the homographs.

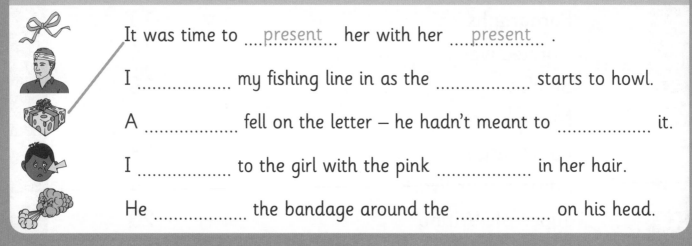

It was time to .....present..... her with her .....present..... .

I .... my fishing line in as the .... starts to howl.

A .... fell on the letter – he hadn't meant to .... it.

I .... to the girl with the pink .... in her hair.

He .... the bandage around the .... on his head.

Write two meanings for each of these homographs.

fly
⇒ To move through the air.
⇒ ....

light
⇒ ....
⇒ ....

content
⇒ ....
⇒ ....

minute
⇒ ....
⇒ ....

Word Play

Sometimes people mix up similar words when writing or speaking.

| Measure the **angel**. | instead of | Measure the **angle**. |

Cross out the word in each sentence that has been used in the wrong way. Write the correct word on the line.

1. You need to be very ~~Pacific~~ when you explain it. ....specific............
2. I jumped out of the tree on porpoise. ....
3. The ship was wrecked when it got caught in a typhoid. ....
4. A fireman's going to check all the fire distinguishers. ....
5. The dancer had a garlic of flowers in her hair. ....

Sometimes people swap the beginning sounds of words when they're speaking. This can be really funny.

| Let's **f**ight a **l**iar. | instead of | Let's **l**ight a **f**ire. |

The beginnings of these words have been mixed up. Rewrite them correctly.

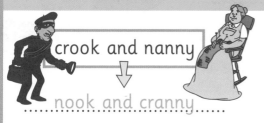

crook and nanny
⬇
nook and cranny

par cark
⬇
....

rough and toothless
⬇
....

mean as custard
⬇
....

Come up with two examples of your own.

....
⬇

....
⬇

....
⬇

Puns

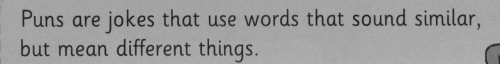

Puns are jokes that use words that sound similar, but mean different things.

> What does a hungry clock do? It goes back four seconds.

Draw lines to match up the two halves of these puns.

| I love puns. | —————— | I think they're really punny. |

Did you hear about the cardboard belt?   It's two-tyred.

The string was told off by its father.   It was a waist of paper.

The bike can't stand up on its own.   It had been knotty.

Write words that sound similar to the words below.

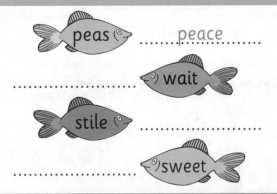

peas ....peace.......

.... wait

stile ....

.... sweet

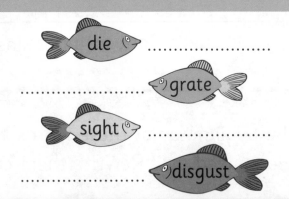

die ....

.... grate

sight ....

.... disgust

Try writing two puns of your own. You can use the words above.

1 ....

....

2 ....

....

Riddles

A riddle is a set of clues that you have to solve.

Here's a 'What am I?' riddle.

I belong to you, but other people use me more than you do.
What am I? **Your name**.

Here's a word-building riddle.

My first is in **w**est but not in east.
My second is in **i**gloo but not in log.
My third is in ta**g** but not in tan.
What am I? A **wig**.

Solve these 'What am I?' riddles.

I carry my home on my back, but I live outside. I'm not rich, but I leave a trail of silver behind me wherever I go.

What am I? ....

What am I?

....

I'm as light as air, but even the strongest person can't hold me for more than a few minutes.

What am I? ....

I'm a cheese that's made backwards.

You can catch me, but you can't throw me.
You can't see me but I'll make you sneeze.

What am I?

....

Solve this word-building riddle.

My first is in stole but not in sole.
My second is in choke but not in cheek.
My third is in goal but not in log.
My fourth is in last but not in tall.
My fifth is in tent but not in never.

What am I? ....

Now write your own.

My first is in .... but not in ....

My second is in .... but not in ....

My third is in .... but not in ....

My fourth is in .... but not in ....

What am I? ....

Prefixes

A prefix is a group of letters that can be added to the beginning of a root word to make a new word.

micro ✚ wave ➡ **micro**wave

Draw a line between each prefix and its meaning.

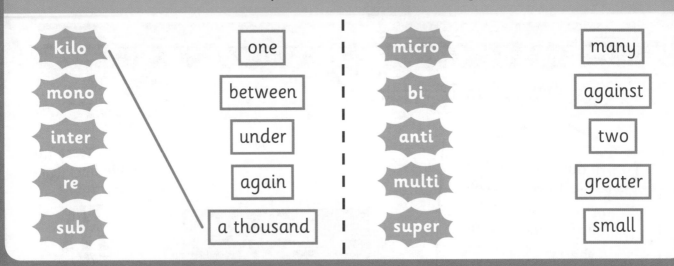

kilo	one
mono	between
inter	under
re	again
sub	a thousand

micro	many
bi	against
anti	two
multi	greater
super	small

Add a prefix to each root word so that it matches its definition.

| anti | inter | multi | mono |

......multi...... storey ➡ A building with lots of levels.

.... rail ➡ A railway with a single rail.

.... freeze ➡ A liquid that stops things from freezing.

.... national ➡ Happening between two or more countries.

Write a word that starts with each of these prefixes.

sub ➡ ......submarine......   micro ➡ ....

bi ➡ ....   re ➡ ....

kilo ➡ ....   super ➡ ....

Suffixes

A suffix is a group of letters that can be added to the end of a root word to make a new word.

terror ➕ **ify** ➡ terr**ify**

Sometimes you need to remove letters from the end of the word before you add the suffix.

Write the root word and the suffix for each of these words.

sadness ➡ .....sad..... ➕ ...ness... | dispensable ➡ .... ➕ ....
cartoonist ➡ .... ➕ .... | leadership ➡ .... ➕ ....
historical ➡ .... ➕ .... | boundary ➡ .... ➕ ....

Cross out all of the words below that have the wrong suffix.

~~povertness~~

magnetism

responsable

tasteful

friendship

venomful

classicous

informatous

shameless

Add a correct suffix to each crossed out word.

............poverty............

....

....

....

....

Circle the suffix in each word. Write a new word using that suffix.

magi(cian) ➡ ....electrician.... | fearsome ➡ ....
falsehood ➡ .... | painless ➡ ....
sadly ➡ .... | dreadful ➡ ....
climber ➡ .... | downward ➡ ....

9

Synonyms and Antonyms

Synonyms are words that mean the same.

big and large

Antonyms are words that mean the opposite.

big and small

Write a synonym or an antonym for each word.

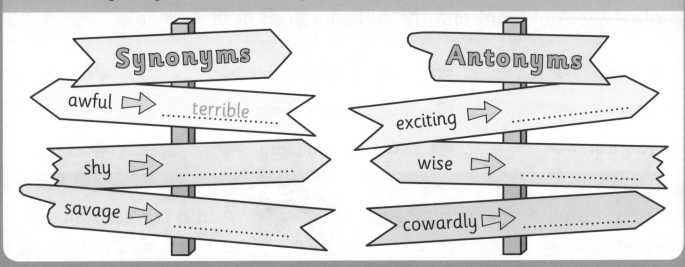

Synonyms

awful ➡ terrible

shy ➡ ....

savage ➡ ....

Antonyms

exciting ➡ ....

wise ➡ ....

cowardly ➡ ....

Finish the crossword with synonyms and antonyms of these words.

Across	Down
Synonyms	Antonyms
3. ~~massive~~	1. ~~correct~~
4. love	2. conflict
6. close by	3. light
8. equal	5. upstairs
10. earth	7. doubt
11. tumble	9. worthless
13. snatch	11. first
14. rock	12. dark

Crossword grid:
- 1 (down) W R O N G
- 3 (across) H U G E
- (Numbers: 1, 2, 3, 4, 5, 6, 7, 8, 9, 10, 11, 12, 13, 14)

Reported Speech

Direct speech is the exact words that someone says.

> "This tree looks very strange," said George.

Direct speech and any punctuation mark is always inside speech marks.

Reported speech is a record of what someone has said.

Reported speech doesn't have speech marks.

> George said that the tree looked very strange.

Change these sentences from direct speech to reported speech.

1 "Give me back my book, Clint!" shouted Jack.

Jack shouted at Clint to give him back his book.

2 Frank said, "I hope Harry's not going to wear those shoes."

....

3 "John, what time did they leave?" asked Mary.

....

4 "People keep phoning me," he moaned. "I'm leaving."

....

Reported speech can be boring if the word 'said' is used too much.
Fill in the gaps in this paragraph using different words for 'said'.

When they got to the park, Shaun ....insisted.......... that he wanted to fly his kite. Adele .... that it was too windy. She ....
that they should go swimming instead. Shaun .... that they never did what he wanted to do. Adele grabbed the kite and .... that she would help him launch it. Shaun picked up the string, ran off and .... that Adele should let go.

Active and Passive

In active sentences, the subject of the sentence **does something** to the object.

The subject

The object

The dog scared **the cow**.

In passive sentences, something is **done to** the subject **by** the object.

The subject

The object

The cow was scared **by the dog**.

Passive sentences often use the word **by**.

Read the sentences below. Put an A in the box next to the active sentences, and a P next to the passive sentences.

1. My watch was broken by my little brother. `P`
2. Charles asked Pamela to the dance. ☐
3. The cake was quickly destroyed by the children. ☐
4. I drew the best picture in the whole gallery. ☐
5. The car was eventually fixed by the mechanic. ☐

Rewrite each sentence above so that the active sentences are passive and the passive sentences are active.

1. My little brother broke my watch.
2. ....
3. ....
4. ....
5. ....

Paragraphs

Dividing your writing into paragraphs makes it easier to read. Start a new paragraph when you start writing about a new subject, when some time has passed or when a new person speaks.

Read this story and put a **/** where a new paragraph should start.

One morning in the holidays, I went to my friend Sahira's house. As she opened the door she cried, "Some ostriches have escaped from the zoo!" "I wonder where they are now," I replied. "Who knows. Shall we go outside?" she asked, and that was that... or so I thought. Later that day, as I walked home, I saw a flock of ostriches chasing a policeman down the street. He only just managed to leap into his car before they stormed past. When I got home, I phoned the zoo and told them where their escaped ostriches were.

Rewrite the story, indenting the first lines of your new paragraphs.

....
....
....
....
....
....
....
....
....
....

Connectives

Connectives are words or phrases that join two parts of a sentence.

I was swimming slowly **when** I saw a shark.

Connectives can also link two separate sentences.

Going swimming in the sea can be dangerous. **For example**, swimmers could be attacked by sharks.

Find twelve connectives in the wordsearch. Write them in the boxes.

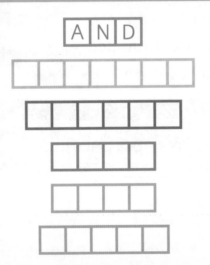

A N D

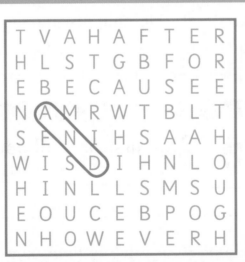

```
T V A H A F T E R
H L S T G B F O R
E B E C A U S E E
N A M R W T B L T
S E N I H S A A H
W I S D I H N L O
H I N L L S M S U
E O U C E B P O G
N H O W E V E R H
```

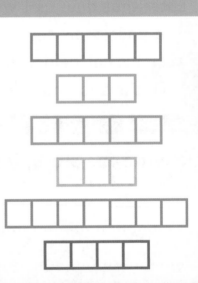

Write sentences using some of the connectives you found.

1 The waiter looked smart because he was wearing a bow tie.

2

3

4

5

6

Underline all of the connectives in the paragraph below.

Making your own greetings card may be simple, <u>but</u> it is
very rewarding. Despite the low cost of materials, finished
cards can look very professional. Consequently, you'll
earn extra brownie points with your friends and family,
especially if you put a lot of time and effort into your card.
Furthermore, if you're not very arty, or you don't have a lot
of time, there are lots of easy but effective designs you can try.

Use the connectives in the box to fill the gaps in these sentences.

| therefore | however | as a result | ~~since~~ | although | meanwhile |

1. ......Since...... my toad had just died, I decided to buy a frog.
   .... , when I got home it ate all of my pet flies.

2. I spent all day trying to find my favourite socks, ... my
   feet weren't cold. .... , my sister was wearing them.

3. Gran's coming to stay, ... we have to clean the house.
   .... , we can't finish our paintings until later.

Write a paragraph about the best day of your life.
Use all the connectives from the box.

| firstly | for instance | yet | finally | moreover | despite |

....
....
....
....
....
....

Similes

A simile is a way of describing something by comparing it to something else. Similes usually use the words **as** or **like**.

> He was **as** cruel **as** the frost in winter.

> Her anger was **like** a volcano erupting.

Underline all of the similes in this paragraph.

She ran through the forest <u>like a fox fleeing from a hunt</u>. The branches of the trees grabbed at her like brittle, twisted hands. Thankfully the moon was bright as she ran, so she could see the path in front of her. Her footsteps were as loud as a stampede of horses and her heart pounded like a drum.

Some similes are overused. Use the pictures to fill in the blanks.

1 The sea was as flat as .... a pancake. ....

2 The girl was as quiet as ....

3 The actor was as cool as ....

4 Her touch was as light as ....

Write your own interesting similes to replace the ones above.

The sea was as flat as .... a rubber dinghy once all the air has been let out. ....

The girl was as quiet as ....

The actor was as cool as ....

The traffic crawled like ....

Practise and Learn

English

Ages 10-11

Answers

This section shows each of the pages from the book with the answers filled out.

The pages are laid out in the same way as the book itself, so the questions can be easily marked by you, or by your child.

There are also helpful learning tips with some of the pages.

---

4 — **Homographs**

Homographs are words that are spelled the same, but have different meanings. ⇨ They had a row about who would row the boat.

Sometimes they sound the same. ⇨ I want to row the blue boat in the second row.

Each sentence is missing two homographs that don't sound the same. Match a picture clue to each sentence and write in the homographs.

It was time to __present__ her with her __present__ .

I __wind__ my fishing line in as the __wind__ starts to howl.

A __tear__ fell on the letter – he hadn't meant to __tear__ it.

I __bow__ to the girl with the pink __bow__ in her hair.

He __wound__ the bandage around the __wound__ on his head.

Write two meanings for each of these homographs.

fly ⇨ To move through the air.
fly ⇨ A small insect with wings.

light ⇨ Something that brightens a room.
light ⇨ Not weighing very much.

content ⇨ Pleased or satisfied.
content ⇨ The things contained in something.

minute ⇨ Very small.
minute ⇨ Sixty seconds.

We've given some examples of definitions, but your child might have written other definitions of these words.

---

5 — **Word Play**

Sometimes people mix up similar words when writing or speaking.

Measure the angel. instead of Measure the angle.

Cross out the word in each sentence that has been used in the wrong way. Write the correct word on the line.

1. You need to be very ~~Pacific~~ when you explain it. ...... specific
2. I jumped out of the tree on ~~porpoise.~~ ...... purpose
3. The ship was wrecked when it got caught in a ~~typhoid.~~ ...... typhoon
4. A fireman's going to check all the fire ~~distinguishers.~~ ...... extinguishers
5. The dancer had a ~~garlic~~ of flowers in her hair. ...... garland

Sometimes people swap the beginning sounds of words when they're speaking. This can be really funny.

Let's fight a liar. instead of Let's light a fire.

The beginnings of these words have been mixed up. Rewrite them correctly.

crook and nanny ⇩ ~~nook and cranny~~

par cark ⇩ car park

rough and toothless ⇩ tough and ruthless

mean as custard ⇩ keen as mustard

Come up with two examples of your own.

⇩ VARIOUS ANSWERS POSSIBLE ⇩

Puns

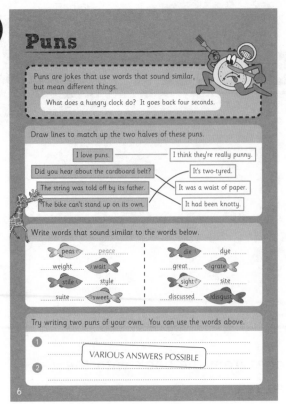

Puns are jokes that use words that sound similar, but mean different things.

What does a hungry clock do? It goes back four seconds.

Draw lines to match up the two halves of these puns.

I love puns.	I think they're really punny.
Did you hear about the cardboard belt?	It's two-tyred.
The string was told off by its father.	It was a waist of paper.
The bike can't stand up on its own.	It had been knotty.

Write words that sound similar to the words below.

peas — *peace*   die — *dye*
weight — *wait*   great — *grate*
stile — *style*   sight — *site*
suite — *sweet*   discussed — *disgust*

Try writing two puns of your own. You can use the words above.

1 .... VARIOUS ANSWERS POSSIBLE
2 ....

If your child muddles up the spelling of words that sound similar, try making a list of tricky words to test them with.

Riddles

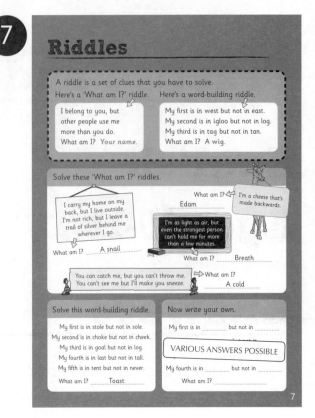

A riddle is a set of clues that you have to solve.
Here's a 'What am I?' riddle.   Here's a word-building riddle.

I belong to you, but other people use me more than you do.
What am I? **Your name.**

My first is in west but not in east.
My second is in igloo but not in log.
My third is in tag but not in tan.
What am I? **A wig.**

Solve these 'What am I?' riddles.

I carry my home on my back, but I live outside. I'm not rich, but I leave a trail of silver behind me wherever I go.
What am I? __A snail__

What am I? __Edam__   I'm a cheese that's made backwards.

I'm as light as air, but even the strongest person can't hold me for more than a few minutes.
What am I? __Breath__

You can catch me, but you can't throw me. You can't see me but I'll make you sneeze.
What am I? __A cold__

Solve this word-building riddle.

My first is in stole but not in sole.
My second is in choke but not in cheek.
My third is in goal but not in log.
My fourth is in last but not in tall.
My fifth is in tent but not in never.
What am I? __Toast__

Now write your own.

My first is in _____ but not in _____.
VARIOUS ANSWERS POSSIBLE
My fourth is in _____ but not in _____.
What am I? _____

Prefixes

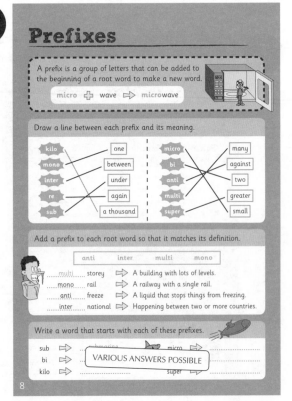

A prefix is a group of letters that can be added to the beginning of a root word to make a new word.

micro ✚ wave ➪ microwave

Draw a line between each prefix and its meaning.

kilo	one	micro	many
mono	between	bi	against
inter	under	anti	two
re	again	multi	greater
sub	a thousand	super	small

Add a prefix to each root word so that it matches its definition.

anti   inter   multi   mono

__multi__ storey ➪ A building with lots of levels.
__mono__ rail ➪ A railway with a single rail.
__anti__ freeze ➪ A liquid that stops things from freezing.
__inter__ national ➪ Happening between two or more countries.

Write a word that starts with each of these prefixes.

sub ➪   micro ➪
bi ➪   VARIOUS ANSWERS POSSIBLE
kilo ➪   super ➪

If your child found it tricky to match the prefixes to their meanings, help them to look up the prefixes in a dictionary or on the internet.

Suffixes

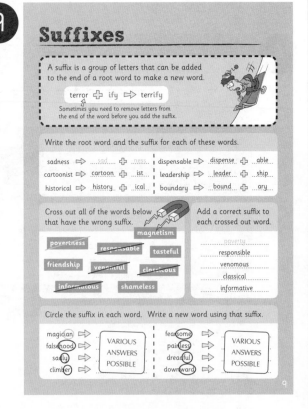

A suffix is a group of letters that can be added to the end of a root word to make a new word.

terror ✚ ify ➪ terrify

Sometimes you need to remove letters from the end of the word before you add the suffix.

Write the root word and the suffix for each of these words.

sadness ➪ __sad__ ✚ __ness__   dispensable ➪ __dispense__ ✚ __able__
cartoonist ➪ __cartoon__ ✚ __ist__   leadership ➪ __leader__ ✚ __ship__
historical ➪ __history__ ✚ __ical__   boundary ➪ __bound__ ✚ __ary__

Cross out all of the words below that have the wrong suffix.

magnetism
~~povertness~~   ~~responsable~~   tasteful
friendship   ~~venemful~~   ~~classious~~
~~informatuous~~   shameless

Add a correct suffix to each crossed out word.

__poverty__
__responsible__
__venomous__
__classical__
__informative__

Circle the suffix in each word. Write a new word using that suffix.

magician ➪
falsehood ➪   VARIOUS ANSWERS POSSIBLE
sadly ➪
climber ➪

fearsome ➪
painless ➪   VARIOUS ANSWERS POSSIBLE
dreadful ➪
downward ➪

10 — Synonyms and Antonyms

Synonyms are words that mean the same.

big and large

Antonyms are words that mean the opposite.

big and small

Write a synonym or an antonym for each word.

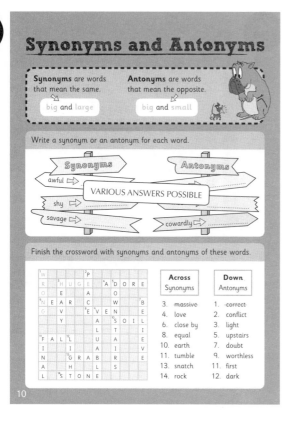

Synonyms

awful ⇨

shy ⇨

savage ⇨

Antonyms

VARIOUS ANSWERS POSSIBLE

cowardly ⇨

Finish the crossword with synonyms and antonyms of these words.

	W				P				
	R	H	U	G	E	A	D	O	R	E
	O		E		A		O		
N	E	A	R		C	W		B
G		V		E	V	E	N		
	Y				A		S	O	I	L
					L		T		I
F	A	L	L		U	A	E
I		I			A	I	V
N		G	R	A	B	R		E
A		H		L		S
L	S	T	O	N	E

Across — Synonyms
3. massive
4. love
6. close by
8. equal
10. earth
11. tumble
13. snatch
14. rock

Down — Antonyms
1. correct
2. conflict
3. light
5. upstairs
7. doubt
9. worthless
11. first
12. dark

10

---

11 — Reported Speech

Direct speech is the exact words that someone says.

"This tree looks very strange," said George.

Direct speech and any punctuation mark is always inside speech marks.

Reported speech is a record of what someone has said.

Reported speech doesn't have speech marks.

George said that the tree looked very strange.

Change these sentences from direct speech to reported speech.

1. "Give me back my book, Clint!" shouted Jack.
   Jack shouted at Clint to give him back his book

2. Frank said, "I hope Harry's not going to wear those shoes."
   Frank said he hoped that Harry wasn't going to wear those shoes.

3. "John, what time did they leave?" asked Mary.
   Mary asked John at what time they left.

4. "People keep phoning me," he moaned. "I'm leaving."
   He moaned that people kept phoning him, so he was leaving.

Reported speech can be boring if the word 'said' is used too much. Fill in the gaps in this paragraph using different words for 'said'.

When they got to the park, Shaun _____insisted_____ that he wanted to fly his kite. Adele _____ that it was too windy. She _____ that they should g_____ VARIOUS ANSWERS POSSIBLE _____ that they never did what he wanted to do. _____ e and _____ that she would help him launch it. Shaun picked up the string, ran off and _____ that Adele should let go.

11

Encourage your child to use a variety of words to replace 'said' — help them to use a thesaurus if they find it difficult to think of suitable words.

---

12 — Active and Passive

In active sentences, the subject of the sentence **does something** to the object.

The subject   *The object*

The dog scared the cow.

In passive sentences, something is **done to** the subject **by** the object.

The subject   *The object*

The cow was scared by the dog.

*Passive sentences often use the word **by**.*

Read the sentences below. Put an A in the box next to the active sentences, and a P next to the passive sentences.

1. My watch was broken by my little brother. [P]
2. Charles asked Pamela to the dance. [A]
3. The cake was quickly destroyed by the children. [P]
4. I drew the best picture in the whole gallery. [A]
5. The car was eventually fixed by the mechanic. [P]

Rewrite each sentence above so that the active sentences are passive and the passive sentences are active.

1. My little brother broke my watch.
2. Pamela was asked to the dance by Charles.
3. The children quickly destroyed the cake.
4. The best picture in the whole gallery was drawn by me.
5. The mechanic eventually fixed the car.

12

---

13 — Paragraphs

Dividing your writing into paragraphs makes it easier to read. Start a new paragraph when you start writing about a new subject, when some time has passed or when a new person speaks.

Read this story and put a / where a new paragraph should start.

One morning in the holidays, I went to my friend Sahira's house. As she opened the door she cried, "Some ostriches have escaped from the zoo!" / "I wonder where they are now," I replied. / "Who knows. Shall we go outside?" she asked, and that was that... so I thought. / Later that day, as I walked home, I saw a flock of ostriches chasing a policeman down the street. He only just managed to leap into his car before they stormed past. / When I got home, I phoned the zoo and told them where their escaped ostriches were.

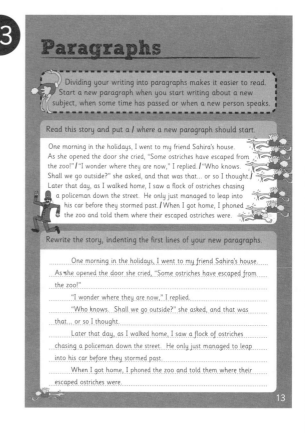

Rewrite the story, indenting the first lines of your new paragraphs.

One morning in the holidays, I went to my friend Sahira's house. As she opened the door she cried, "Some ostriches have escaped from the zoo!"

"I wonder where they are now," I replied.

"Who knows. Shall we go outside?" she asked, and that was that... or so I thought.

Later that day, as I walked home, I saw a flock of ostriches chasing a policeman down the street. He only just managed to leap into his car before they stormed past.

When I got home, I phoned the zoo and told them where their escaped ostriches were.

13

14 Connectives

Connectives are words or phrases that join two parts of a sentence.

> I was swimming slowly **when** I saw a shark.

Connectives can also link two separate sentences.

> Going swimming in the sea can be dangerous. **For example,** swimmers could be attacked by sharks.

Find twelve connectives in the wordsearch. Write them in the boxes.

AND
BECAUSE
THOUGH
THEN
WHEN
WHILE

AFTER
FOR
SINCE
BUT
HOWEVER
ALSO

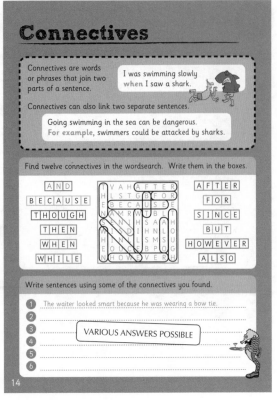

Write sentences using some of the connectives you found.

1. The waiter looked smart because he was wearing a bow tie.
2. ......
3. ...... VARIOUS ANSWERS POSSIBLE
4. ......
5. ......
6. ......

14

You could extend this exercise by getting your child to write sentences that contain more than one connective.

15

Underline all of the connectives in the paragraph below.

Making your own greetings card may be simple, <u>but</u> it is very rewarding. <u>Despite</u> the low cost of materials, finished cards can look very professional. <u>Consequently</u>, you'll earn extra brownie points with your friends and family, <u>especially</u> if you put a lot of time and effort into your card. <u>Furthermore</u>, if you're not very arty, <u>or</u> you don't have a lot of time, there are lots of easy but effective designs you can try.

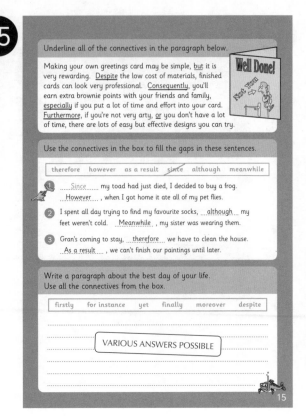

Use the connectives in the box to fill the gaps in these sentences.

| therefore | however | as a result | since | although | meanwhile |

1. __Since__ my toad had just died, I decided to buy a frog. __However__, when I got home it ate all of my pet flies.
2. I spent all day trying to find my favourite socks, __although__ my feet weren't cold. __Meanwhile__, my sister was wearing them.
3. Gran's coming to stay, __therefore__ we have to clean the house. __As a result__, we can't finish our paintings until later.

Write a paragraph about the best day of your life. Use all the connectives from the box.

| firstly | for instance | yet | finally | moreover | despite |

...... VARIOUS ANSWERS POSSIBLE ......

15

---

16 Similes

A simile is a way of describing something by comparing it to something else. Similes usually use the words **as** or **like**.

> He was **as** cruel **as** the frost in winter.

> Her anger was **like** a volcano erupting.

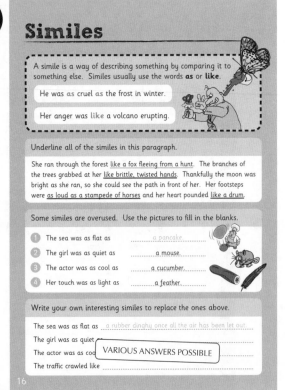

Underline all of the similes in this paragraph.

She ran through the forest <u>like a fox fleeing from a hunt</u>. The branches of the trees grabbed at her <u>like brittle, twisted hands</u>. Thankfully the moon was bright as she ran, so she could see the path in front of her. Her footsteps were <u>as loud as a stampede of horses</u> and her heart pounded <u>like a drum</u>.

Some similes are overused. Use the pictures to fill in the blanks.

1. The sea was as flat as __a pancake__.
2. The girl was as quiet as __a mouse__.
3. The actor was as cool as __a cucumber__.
4. Her touch was as light as __a feather__.

Write your own interesting similes to replace the ones above.

The sea was as flat as __a rubber dinghy once all the air has been let out__
The girl was as quiet ...
The actor was as cool ... VARIOUS ANSWERS POSSIBLE
The traffic crawled like ...

16

---

17 Metaphors

Metaphors describe something as if it is something else.

> His feet **were** springs, launching him into the air.

Underline the metaphors in this paragraph.

Sanjay's <u>hands were blocks of ice</u> as he waited for the whistle. His <u>stomach was a monster</u> twisting around inside him, and he felt as scared as a cornered mouse. His <u>tongue was a dry sponge</u> inside his mouth, and his feet felt as heavy as iron anvils. The whistle sounded and Sanjay dived. His <u>body was a knife</u> slicing through the water.

Write your own metaphors on the lines below.

1. The dancer is __a firework exploding on the stage__
2. My fear was ...
3. The jewels a... VARIOUS ANSWERS POSSIBLE
4. The pudding was ...
5. His hair is ...

Write a paragraph about your favourite holiday using five metaphors.

...... VARIOUS ANSWERS POSSIBLE ......

17

Children often get metaphors and similes confused. Make sure your child has used metaphors rather than similes in these exercises.

18. Punctuation

Using the right punctuation makes your writing easier to understand.

Those mice are my parents'. means The mice belong to my parents.

Those mice are my parents. means My parents are mice.

Rewrite these sentences, adding in the missing punctuation.

1. ive completely run out of cat food for my lion roger
   I've completely run out of cat food for my lion, Roger.

2. i cant believe you did that shouted mike angrily
   "I can't believe you did that!" shouted Mike angrily.

3. at the supermarket i bought tomatoes grapes and plums
   At the supermarket I bought tomatoes, grapes and plums.

4. caseys excited because were going to maggies house
   Casey's excited because we're going to Maggie's house.

Write a paragraph about your favourite thing to do at the weekend. Use each punctuation mark on the sign at least once.

VARIOUS ANSWERS POSSIBLE

Encourage your child to use varied and accurate punctuation whenever they're writing.

19. Editing Your Work

When you've finished writing something, make sure it doesn't have any mistakes in. Add, cross out or change words to make it sound better.

On Saturday morning I'm going to the skate park with my friends Celeste and John. ~~and we're planning~~ to stay there all day, ~~or at least until the afternoon.~~

> Divide sentences that are too long into two shorter ones.
> Cross out bits that don't add anything to the story.

Correct two spelling or punctuation mistakes in each sentence.

1. The goats we're [were] secretly planning a revolution [revolution].
2. The multiplies [multiples] of four and eight are all even numbers [.]
3. ~~S~~Salamanders are very loyal so they make brilliant pets [pets].
4. Blue potatoes [potatoes] are very nutritious if your [you're] a giraffe.

Cross out the information that isn't relevant in the paragraph below.

Last weekend I went to my grandad's 94th birthday party ~~at 3pm on Saturday~~ at the village hall and there was dancing and cake ~~and I was happy because it was chocolate cake and that is my favourite sort of cake~~. My cousin, ~~who used to live on a farm~~, came ~~to my grandad's 94th birthday party which was at the village hall~~ and all the family came and brought grandad presents ~~and my present was the best one of all~~ and my grandad had a really good time.

Rewrite the paragraph above, leaving out the irrelevant information, and shortening sentences where you need to.

Last weekend I went to my grandad's 94th birthday party. It was at the village hall, and there was dancing and cake. My cousin came, and so did all the family. We all brought grandad presents and he had a really good time.

OTHER ANSWERS POSSIBLE

Your child might have decided that different bits of text were relevant — that's fine, as long as what they've written makes sense and isn't repetitive.

20. Types of Writing

You can change one type of writing into a different type.

Biography is about someone else's life.
Sam used to stick her tongue out at tigers. ⇨ I stuck my tongue out at the tiger.

Autobiography is about the writer's own life.

Instructions tell you what to do.
Stick your tongue out at a tiger. ⇨ You should stick your tongue out at a tiger — it's fun!

Persuasion convinces you to do something.

Write the type of writing used in each of these books.

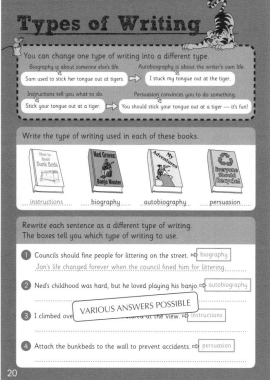

instructions biography autobiography persuasion

Rewrite each sentence as a different type of writing. The boxes tell you which type of writing to use.

1. Councils should fine people for littering on the street. ⇨ biography
   Jon's life changed forever when the council fined him for littering.

2. Ned's childhood was hard, but he loved playing his banjo ⇨ autobiography

   VARIOUS ANSWERS POSSIBLE

3. I climbed over ... stared at the view. ⇨ instructions

4. Attach the bunkbeds to the wall to prevent accidents. ⇨ persuasion

21

Read the paragraph below, then answer the questions.

> Children should all be given free unicycling lessons. They are spending too much time watching television, surfing the internet, or playing on games consoles. This disastrous trend cannot be allowed to continue. Children need regular exercise. They enjoy sports that are challenging and fun. No sport is more challenging or more fun than unicycling!

1. What type of writing is this? Persuasive
2. How can you tell?
   You can tell that the text is persuasive because it is trying to convince readers that children should have unicycling lessons.
3. Are these sentences facts or opinions?

   Children need regular exercise. ⇨ Fact

   No sport is more challenging or more fun than unicycling! ⇨ Opinion

Read the paragraph below, then answer the questions.

> Many people think that unicycles came from the penny-farthing bicycle. Some riders removed the small back wheel and rode on just the large front wheel. Modern unicycling is very varied. Mountain unicycling involves riding down steep mountain trails at high speeds, and unicycle hockey is just like roller hockey, but each player rides a unicycle. Some people even ride their unicycles to work!

1. What type of writing is this? Information
2. How can you tell?
   You can tell that the text is informative because it gives the reader lots of facts about unicycles.
3. Is it mainly made up of facts or opinions? Facts

Poems

Poets use words to create atmosphere, paint a picture or get across a message. Read this poem and answer the questions on the next page.

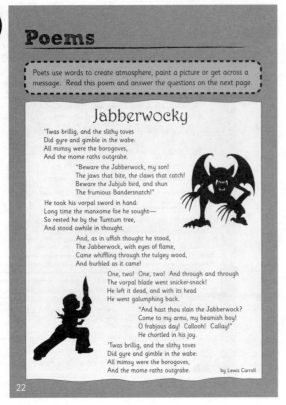

Jabberwocky

'Twas brillig, and the slithy toves
Did gyre and gimble in the wabe:
All mimsy were the borogoves,
And the mome raths outgrabe.

"Beware the Jabberwock, my son!
The jaws that bite, the claws that catch!
Beware the Jubjub bird, and shun
The frumious Bandersnatch!"

He took his vorpal sword in hand:
Long time the manxome foe he sought—
So rested he by the Tumtum tree,
And stood awhile in thought.

And, as in uffish thought he stood,
The Jabberwock, with eyes of flame,
Came whiffling through the tulgey wood,
And burbled as it came!

One, two! One, two! And through and through
The vorpal blade went snicker-snack!
He left it dead, and with its head
He went galumphing back.

"And hast thou slain the Jabberwock?
Come to my arms, my beamish boy!
O frabjous day! Callooh! Callay!"
He chortled in his joy.

'Twas brillig, and the slithy toves
Did gyre and gimble in the wabe:
All mimsy were the borogoves,
And the mome raths outgrabe.

by Lewis Carroll

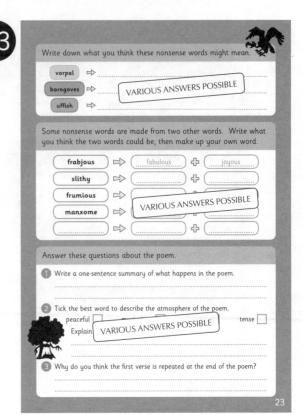

Write down what you think these nonsense words might mean.

vorpal ⇒ ....
borogoves ⇒ VARIOUS ANSWERS POSSIBLE
uffish ⇒ ....

Some nonsense words are made from two other words. Write what you think the two words could be, then make up your own word.

frabjous ⇒ (fabulous) ✚ (joyous)
slithy ⇒ ( ) ✚ ( )
frumious ⇒ ( ) ✚ ( )
manxome ⇒ VARIOUS ANSWERS POSSIBLE
( ) ⇒ ( ) ✚ ( )

Answer these questions about the poem.

1 Write a one-sentence summary of what happens in the poem.
....

2 Tick the best word to describe the atmosphere of the poem.
peaceful ☐   VARIOUS ANSWERS POSSIBLE   tense ☐
Explain ....

3 Why do you think the first verse is repeated at the end of the poem?
....

To challenge your child further, ask them to pick out specific examples from the poem to explain why they did or didn't enjoy it.

Reading an Extract

Read this extract from 'The Secret Garden' by Frances Hodgson Burnett.

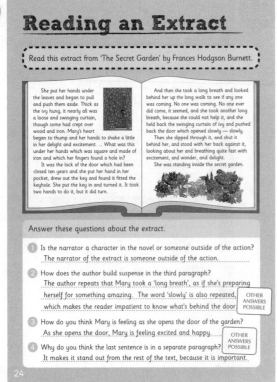

She put her hands under the leaves and began to pull and push them aside. Thick as the ivy hung, it nearly all was a loose and swinging curtain, though some had crept over wood and iron. Mary's heart began to thump and her hands to shake a little in her delight and excitement. ... What was this under her hands which was square and made of iron and which her fingers found a hole in?

It was the lock of the door which had been closed ten years and she put her hand in her pocket, drew out the key and found it fitted the keyhole. She put the key in and turned it. It took two hands to do it, but it did turn.

And then she took a long breath and looked behind her up the long walk to see if any one was coming. No one was coming. No one ever did come, it seemed, and she took another long breath, because she could not help it, and she held back the swinging curtain of ivy and pushed back the door which opened slowly — slowly.

Then she slipped through it, and shut it behind her, and stood with her back against it, looking about her and breathing quite fast with excitement, and wonder, and delight.

She was standing inside the secret garden.

Answer these questions about the extract.

1 Is the narrator a character in the novel or someone outside of the action?
The narrator of the extract is someone outside of the action.

2 How does the author build suspense in the third paragraph?
The author repeats that Mary took a 'long breath', as if she's preparing herself for something amazing. The word 'slowly' is also repeated, which makes the reader impatient to know what's behind the door.
OTHER ANSWERS POSSIBLE

3 How do you think Mary is feeling as she opens the door of the garden?
As she opens the door, Mary is feeling excited and happy.
OTHER ANSWERS POSSIBLE

4 Why do you think the last sentence is in a separate paragraph?
It makes it stand out from the rest of the text, because it is important.

Your child may have come up with different answers for questions 2, 3 and 4 — that's fine as long as they've shown that they understand the text.

Persuasive Writing

Persuasive writing tries to convince the reader to do something.

Here's what the writer wants you to do.   Statistics are often used to persuade people.   Persuasive writing often contains arguments.

Buy 'Flawless Floors' cleaner today. It kills 99% of bacteria. It's cheaper than other floor cleaners, and it'll keep your whole family safe from germs.   Some persuasive writing appeals to your emotions to convince you

Read this article and then answer the questions below.

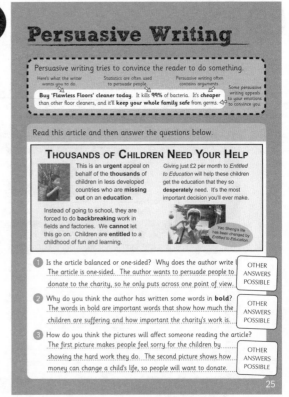

THOUSANDS OF CHILDREN NEED YOUR HELP

This is an urgent appeal on behalf of the thousands of children in less developed countries who are missing out on an education.

Instead of going to school, they are forced to do backbreaking work in fields and factories. We cannot let this go on. Children are entitled to a childhood of fun and learning.

Giving just £2 per month to Entitled to Education will help these children get the education that they so desperately need. It's the most important decision you'll ever make.

Yao Sheng's life has been changed by Entitled to Education.

1 Is the article balanced or one-sided? Why does the author write l
The article is one-sided. The author wants to persuade people to donate to the charity, so he only puts across one point of view.
OTHER ANSWERS POSSIBLE

2 Why do you think the author has written some words in bold?
The words in bold are important words that show how much the children are suffering and how important the charity's work is.
OTHER ANSWERS POSSIBLE

3 How do you think the pictures will affect someone reading the article?
The first picture makes people feel sorry for the children by showing the hard work they do. The second picture shows how money can change a child's life, so people will want to donate.
OTHER ANSWERS POSSIBLE

If your child found the final question difficult, ask them to think about how the pictures make **them** feel.

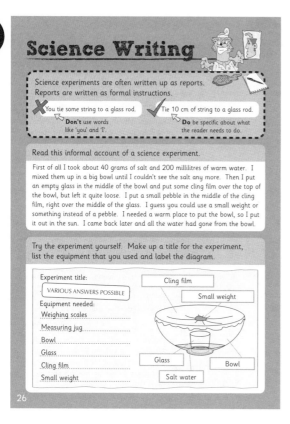

Science Writing

Science experiments are often written up as reports.
Reports are written as formal instructions.

✗ You tie some string to a glass rod.
Don't use words like 'you' and 'I'.

✓ Tie 10 cm of string to a glass rod.
Do be specific about what the reader needs to do.

Read this informal account of a science experiment.

First of all I took about 40 grams of salt and 200 millilitres of warm water. I mixed them up in a big bowl until I couldn't see the salt any more. Then I put an empty glass in the middle of the bowl and put some cling film over the top of the bowl, but left it quite loose. I put a small pebble in the middle of the cling film, right over the middle of the glass. I guess you could use a small weight or something instead of a pebble. I needed a warm place to put the bowl, so I put it out in the sun. I came back later and all the water had gone from the bowl.

Try the experiment yourself. Make up a title for the experiment, list the equipment that you used and label the diagram.

Experiment title:
VARIOUS ANSWERS POSSIBLE
Equipment needed:
Weighing scales
Measuring jug
Bowl
Glass
Cling film
Small weight

Cling film
Small weight
Glass
Salt water
Bowl

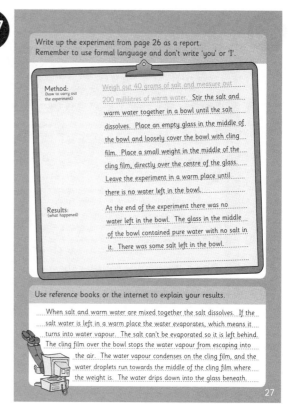

Write up the experiment from page 26 as a report.
Remember to use formal language and don't write 'you' or 'I'.

Method:
(how to carry out the experiment)
Weigh out 40 grams of salt and measure out 200 millilitres of warm water. Stir the salt and warm water together in a bowl until the salt dissolves. Place an empty glass in the middle of the bowl and loosely cover the bowl with cling film. Place a small weight in the middle of the cling film, directly over the centre of the glass. Leave the experiment in a warm place until there is no water left in the bowl.

Results:
(what happened)
At the end of the experiment there was no water left in the bowl. The glass in the middle of the bowl contained pure water with no salt in it. There was some salt left in the bowl.

Use reference books or the internet to explain your results.

When salt and warm water are mixed together the salt dissolves. If the salt water is left in a warm place the water evaporates, which means it turns into water vapour. The salt can't be evaporated so it is left behind. The cling film over the bowl stops the water vapour from escaping into the air. The water vapour condenses on the cling film, and the water droplets run towards the middle of the cling film where the weight is. The water drips down into the glass beneath.

Encourage your child to write things in their own words rather than copying directly from reference books or the internet.

A Classic Text

Read this extract from 'Anne of Green Gables' by L.M. Montgomery.

Marilla set the candle on a three-legged, three-cornered table and turned down the bedclothes. "I suppose you have a nightgown?" she questioned.
Anne nodded. "Yes, I have two. The matron of the asylum* made them for me. They're fearfully skimpy. There is never enough to go around in an asylum, so things are always skimpy — at least in a poor asylum like ours. I hate skimpy night-dresses. But one can dream just as well in them as in lovely trailing ones, with frills around the neck, that's one consolation."
"Well, undress as quick as you can and go to bed. I'll come back in a few minutes for the candle. I daren't trust you to put it out yourself. You'd likely set the place on fire."
When Marilla had gone Anne looked around her wistfully. The whitewashed walls were so painfully bare and staring that she thought they must ache over their own bareness... With a sob she hastily discarded her garments, put on the skimpy nightgown and sprang into bed where she burrowed face downward into the pillow and pulled the clothes over her head.

*orphanage

Answer these questions about the extract above.

1. Why is Anne's nightgown skimpy?
   There was not enough material in the orphanage for a better nightgown.

2. Why does Marilla say she'll come back for the candle later?
   She doesn't trust Anne. She thinks Anne will start a fire.

3. How does Anne feel after Marilla leaves? How can you tell?
   Anne feels sad. She feels sorry for the bare walls and she wishes she was somewhere nicer.

4. How does the language in the extract show that it is from an old novel?
   The language is old-fashioned, for example words such as "asylum", "whitewashed" and "nightgown" aren't used much any more. The characters are also using candles instead of electric lights.

Encourage your child to back up their answers with quotes from the text — it's a good habit to get into.

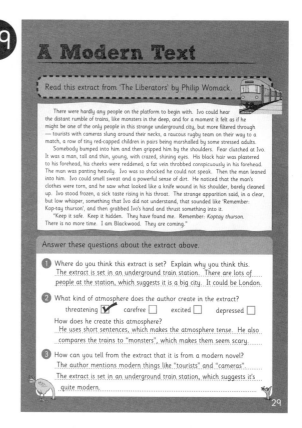

A Modern Text

Read this extract from 'The Liberators' by Philip Womack.

There were hardly any people on the platform to begin with. Ivo could hear the distant rumble of trains, like monsters in the deep, and for a moment it felt as if he might be one of the only people in this strange underground city, but more filtered through — tourists with cameras slung around their necks, a raucous rugby team on their way to a match, a row of tiny red-capped children in pairs being marshalled by some stressed adults.
Somebody bumped into him and then gripped him by the shoulders. Fear clutched at Ivo. It was a man, tall and thin, young, with crazed, shining eyes. His black hair was plastered to his forehead, his cheeks were reddened; a fat vein throbbed conspicuously in his forehead. The man was panting heavily. Ivo was so shocked he could not speak. Then the man leaned into him. Ivo could smell sweat and a powerful sense of dirt. He noticed that the man's clothes were torn, and he saw what looked like a knife wound in his shoulder, barely cleaned up. Ivo stood frozen, a sick taste rising in his throat. The strange apparition said, in a clear, but low whisper, something that Ivo did not understand, that sounded like 'Remember: Kop-tay thurson', and then grabbed Ivo's hand and thrust something into it.
"Keep it safe. Keep it hidden. They have found me. Remember: *Koptay thurson*. There is no more time. I am Blackwood. They are coming."

Answer these questions about the extract above.

1. Where do you think this extract is set? Explain why you think this.
   The extract is set in an underground train station. There are lots of people at the station, which suggests it is a big city. It could be London.

2. What kind of atmosphere does the author create in the extract?
   threatening ✓   carefree ☐   excited ☐   depressed ☐
   How does he create this atmosphere?
   He uses short sentences, which makes the atmosphere tense. He also compares the trains to "monsters", which makes them seem scary.

3. How can you tell from the extract that it is from a modern novel?
   The author mentions modern things like "tourists" and "cameras". The extract is set in an underground train station, which suggests it's quite modern.

Comparing Texts

Sometimes you need to compare two different texts.

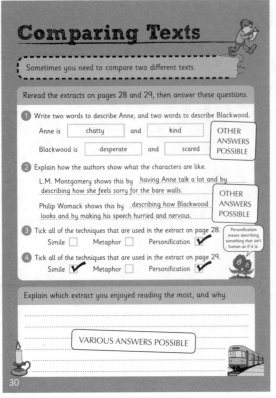

Reread the extracts on pages 28 and 29, then answer these questions.

1 Write two words to describe Anne, and two words to describe Blackwood.

Anne is [chatty] and [kind]

Blackwood is [desperate] and [scared]

OTHER ANSWERS POSSIBLE

2 Explain how the authors show what the characters are like.

L.M. Montgomery shows this by _having Anne talk a lot and by describing how she feels sorry for the bare walls._

Philip Womack shows this by _describing how Blackwood looks and by making his speech hurried and nervous._

OTHER ANSWERS POSSIBLE

3 Tick all of the techniques that are used in the extract on page 28.

Simile [ ]   Metaphor [ ]   Personification [✓]

Personification means describing something that isn't human as if it is.

4 Tick all of the techniques that are used in the extract on page 29.

Simile [✓]   Metaphor [ ]   Personification [✓]

Explain which extract you enjoyed reading the most, and why.

....

VARIOUS ANSWERS POSSIBLE

....

30

Ask your child to explain which aspects of the extracts they liked best, e.g. the characters, the setting or the way the text is written.

Reading Dialects

A dialect is a type of language that's used in a particular region. It uses words and phrases that aren't part of standard English.

Match the dialect words with what you think they mean. Use the internet to help you if you get stuck.

(beck) [grumpy] (barney) [stream] (grockle)

[tourist] (owt) [anything] (mardy) [argument]

Read this extract and then answer the questions.

You don't know about me without you have read a book by the name of 'The Adventures of Tom Sawyer'; but that ain't no matter. That book was made by Mr. Mark Twain, and he told the truth, mainly. There was things which he stretched, but mainly he told the truth. That is nothing. I never seen anybody but lied one time or another, without it was Aunt Polly, or the widow, or maybe Mary. Aunt Polly — Tom's Aunt Polly, she is — and Mary, and the Widow Douglas, is all told about in that book, which is mostly a true book; with some stretchers, as I said before.

From 'The Adventures of Huckleberry Finn', by Mark Twain

1 Can you work out what these words from the extract mean?

stretchers — lies   without it was — unless it was

2 Rewrite "there was things which he stretched" in standard English.

There were some things which he lied about.

3 Why do you think Mark Twain used dialect in his book?

Mark Twain used dialect to make his characters seem like real people, and to show the reader how the characters talked.

31

Book Reviews

You write book reviews to say what you think of books you've read.

Write a book review of a fiction book you've read. Use examples from the book to back up your answers.

Title: ....

Author: ....

Plot: ....

VARIOUS ANSWERS POSSIBLE

....

Who was your favourite character? ....

How did this character develop through the book?

....

VARIOUS ANSWERS POSSIBLE

....

What did you like about the author's style?

Draw your own cover for the book here.

VARIOUS ANSWERS POSSIBLE

....

Write two sentences persuading a friend to read it.

....

VARIOUS ANSWERS POSSIBLE

32

Encourage your child to think critically about books they've read — it's an important skill to develop.

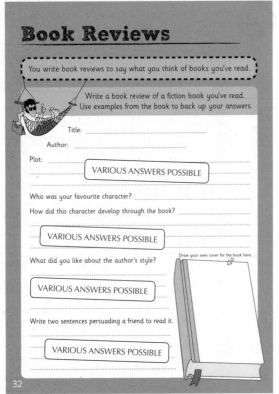

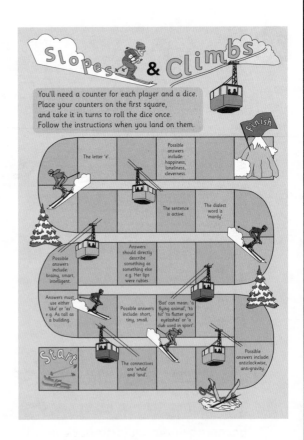

Slopes & Climbs

You'll need a counter for each player and a dice. Place your counters on the first square, and take it in turns to roll the dice once. Follow the instructions when you land on them.

Finish

The letter 'e'.

Possible answers include: happiness, loneliness, cleverness.

The sentence is active.

The dialect word is 'mardy'.

Answers should directly describe something as something else e.g. Her lips were rubies.

Possible answers include: brainy, smart, intelligent.

Answers must use either 'like' or 'as' e.g. As tall as a building.

Possible answers include: short, tiny, small.

'Bat' can mean: 'a flying animal', 'to hit' 'to flutter your eyelashes' or 'a club used in sport'.

Start

The connectives are 'while' and 'and'.

Possible answers include: anticlockwise, anti-gravity.

Metaphors

Metaphors describe something as if it is something else.

> His feet **were** springs, launching him into the air.

Underline the metaphors in this paragraph.

Sanjay's <u>hands were blocks of ice</u> as he waited for the whistle. His stomach was a monster twisting around inside him, and he felt as scared as a cornered mouse. His tongue was a dry sponge inside his mouth, and his feet felt as heavy as iron anvils. The whistle sounded and Sanjay dived. His body was a knife slicing through the water.

Write your own metaphors on the lines below.

1. The dancer is _a firework exploding on the stage._
2. My fear was ....
3. The jewels are ....
4. The pudding was ....
5. His hair is ....

Write a paragraph about your favourite holiday using five metaphors.

....
....
....
....
....
....

17

Punctuation

Using the right punctuation makes your writing easier to understand.

| Those mice are my parents'. | means | The mice belong to my parents. |
| Those mice are my parents. | means | My parents are mice. |

Rewrite these sentences, adding in the missing punctuation.

1. ive completely run out of cat food for my lion roger

   I've completely run out of cat food for my lion, Roger.

2. i cant believe you did that shouted mike angrily

   ....

3. at the supermarket i bought tomatoes grapes and plums

   ....

4. caseys excited because were going to maggies house

   ....

Write a paragraph about your favourite thing to do at the weekend. Use each punctuation mark on the sign at least once.

....
....
....
....
....
....

Editing Your Work

When you've finished writing something, make sure it doesn't have any mistakes in. Add, cross out or change words to make it sound better.

On Saturday morning I'm going to the skate park with my friends Celeste and John. ~~and~~ Ẇe're planning to stay there all day, ~~or at least until the afternoon.~~

Divide sentences that are too long into two shorter ones.

Cross out bits that don't add anything to the story.

Correct two spelling or punctuation mistakes in each sentence.

1. The goats ~~we're~~ were secretly planning a ~~revolusion~~ revolution.

2. The multiplies of four and eight are all even numbers

3. salamanders are very loyal so they make brilliant pet's.

4. Blue potatos are very nutritious if your a giraffe.

Cross out the information that isn't relevant in the paragraph below.

Last weekend I went to my grandad's 94th birthday party ~~at 3pm on Saturday~~ at the village hall and there was dancing and cake and I was happy because it was chocolate cake and that is my favourite sort of cake. My cousin, who used to live on a farm, came to my grandad's 94th birthday party which was at the village hall and all the family came and brought grandad presents and my present was the best one of all and my grandad had a really good time.

Rewrite the paragraph above, leaving out the irrelevant information, and shortening sentences where you need to.

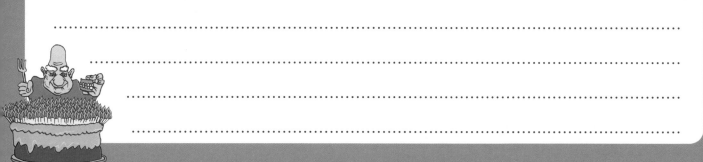

....

....

....

....

Types of Writing

You can change one type of writing into a different type.

Biography is about someone else's life.

Sam used to stick her tongue out at tigers. I stuck my tongue out at the tiger.

Autobiography is about the writer's own life.

Instructions tell you what to do.

Stick your tongue out at a tiger.

Persuasion convinces you to do something.

You should stick your tongue out at a tiger — it's fun!

Write the type of writing used in each of these books.

....

Rewrite each sentence as a different type of writing.
The boxes tell you which type of writing to use.

1 Councils should fine people for littering on the street. → biography

Jon's life changed forever when the council fined him for littering.

2 Ned's childhood was hard, but he loved playing his banjo. → autobiography

....

3 I climbed over the boulder and stared at the view. → instructions

....

4 Attach the bunkbeds to the wall to prevent accidents. → persuasion

....

20

Read the paragraph below, then answer the questions.

> Children should all be given free unicycling lessons. They are spending too much time watching television, surfing the internet, or playing on games consoles. This disastrous trend cannot be allowed to continue. Children need regular exercise. They enjoy sports that are challenging and fun. No sport is more challenging or more fun than unicycling!

1 What type of writing is this? ....

2 How can you tell?

....

....

3 Are these sentences facts or opinions?

| Children need regular exercise. | ⟹ | .... |

| No sport is more challenging or more fun than unicycling! | ⟹ | .... |

Read the paragraph below, then answer the questions.

> Many people think that unicycles came from the penny-farthing bicycle. Some riders removed the small back wheel and rode on just the large front wheel. Modern unicycling is very varied. Mountain unicycling involves riding down steep mountain trails at high speeds, and unicycle hockey is just like roller hockey, but each player rides a unicycle. Some people even ride their unicycles to work!

1 What type of writing is this? ....

2 How can you tell?

....

....

3 Is it mainly made up of facts or opinions? ....

21

Poems

Poets use words to create atmosphere, paint a picture or get across a message. Read this poem and answer the questions on the next page.

Jabberwocky

'Twas brillig, and the slithy toves
Did gyre and gimble in the wabe:
All mimsy were the borogoves,
And the mome raths outgrabe.

"Beware the Jabberwock, my son!
The jaws that bite, the claws that catch!
Beware the Jubjub bird, and shun
The frumious Bandersnatch!"

He took his vorpal sword in hand:
Long time the manxome foe he sought—
So rested he by the Tumtum tree,
And stood awhile in thought.

And, as in uffish thought he stood,
The Jabberwock, with eyes of flame,
Came whiffling through the tulgey wood,
And burbled as it came!

One, two! One, two! And through and through
The vorpal blade went snicker-snack!
He left it dead, and with its head
He went galumphing back.

"And hast thou slain the Jabberwock?
Come to my arms, my beamish boy!
O frabjous day! Callooh! Callay!"
He chortled in his joy.

'Twas brillig, and the slithy toves
Did gyre and gimble in the wabe:
All mimsy were the borogoves,
And the mome raths outgrabe.

by Lewis Carroll

Write down what you think these nonsense words might mean.

vorpal ⇨ ....

borogoves ⇨ ....

uffish ⇨ ....

Some nonsense words are made from two other words. Write what you think the two words could be, then make up your own word.

frabjous	⇨	fabulous	⊹	joyous
slithy	⇨	....	⊹	....
frumious	⇨	....	⊹	....
manxome	⇨	....	⊹	....
....	⇨	....	⊹	....

Answer these questions about the poem.

① Write a one-sentence summary of what happens in the poem.

....

....

② Tick the best word to describe the atmosphere of the poem.

peaceful ☐   mysterious ☐   exciting ☐   tense ☐

Explain why you chose this word.

....

....

③ Why do you think the first verse is repeated at the end of the poem?

....

....

Reading an Extract

Read this extract from 'The Secret Garden' by Frances Hodgson Burnett.

She put her hands under the leaves and began to pull and push them aside. Thick as the ivy hung, it nearly all was a loose and swinging curtain, though some had crept over wood and iron. Mary's heart  began to thump and her hands to shake a little in her delight and excitement. ... What was this under her hands which was square and made of iron and which her fingers found a hole in?

It was the lock of the door which had been closed ten years and she put her hand in her pocket, drew out the key and found it fitted the keyhole. She put the key in and turned it. It took two hands to do it, but it did turn.

And then she took a long breath and looked behind her up the long walk to see if any one was coming. No one was coming. No one ever did come, it seemed, and she took another long breath, because she could not help it, and she held back the swinging curtain of ivy and pushed back the door which opened slowly — slowly.

Then she slipped through it, and shut it behind her, and stood with her back against it, looking about her and breathing quite fast with excitement, and wonder, and delight.

She was standing inside the secret garden.

Answer these questions about the extract.

1. Is the narrator a character in the novel or someone outside of the action?

....

2. How does the author build suspense in the third paragraph?

....

....

....

3. How do you think Mary is feeling as she opens the door of the garden?

....

4. Why do you think the last sentence is in a separate paragraph?

....

24

Persuasive Writing

Read this article and then answer the questions below.

THOUSANDS OF CHILDREN NEED YOUR HELP

This is an **urgent** appeal on behalf of the **thousands** of children in less developed countries who are **missing out** on an **education**.

Instead of going to school, they are forced to do **backbreaking** work in fields and factories. We **cannot** let this go on. Children are **entitled** to a childhood of fun and learning.

Giving just £2 per month to *Entitled to Education* will help these children get the education that they so **desperately** need. It's the most important decision you'll ever make.

Yao Sheng's life has been changed by *Entitled to Education*.

1 Is the article balanced or one-sided? Why does the author write like this?

....

....

2 Why do you think the author has written some words in **bold**?

....

....

3 How do you think the pictures will affect someone reading the article?

....

....

....

Science Writing

Science experiments are often written up as reports.
Reports are written as formal instructions.

✗ You tie some string to a glass rod.

Don't use words like 'you' and 'I'.

✓ Tie 10 cm of string to a glass rod.

Do be specific about what the reader needs to do.

Read this informal account of a science experiment.

First of all I took about 40 grams of salt and 200 millilitres of warm water. I mixed them up in a big bowl until I couldn't see the salt any more. Then I put an empty glass in the middle of the bowl and put some cling film over the top of the bowl, but left it quite loose. I put a small pebble in the middle of the cling film, right over the middle of the glass. I guess you could use a small weight or something instead of a pebble. I needed a warm place to put the bowl, so I put it out in the sun. I came back later and all the water had gone from the bowl.

Try the experiment yourself. Make up a title for the experiment, list the equipment that you used and label the diagram.

Experiment title:

....

Equipment needed:

....

....

....

....

....

Write up the experiment from page 26 as a report.
Remember to use formal language and don't write 'you' or 'I'.

Method:
(how to carry out
the experiment)

Weigh out 40 grams of salt and measure out
200 millilitres of warm water.

....

....

....

....

....

....

....

....

Results:
(what happened)

....

....

....

....

....

Use reference books or the internet to explain your results.

....

....

....

....

....

....

A Classic Text

Read this extract from 'Anne of Green Gables' by L.M. Montgomery.

Marilla set the candle on a three-legged, three-cornered table and turned down the bedclothes. "I suppose you have a nightgown?" she questioned.

Anne nodded. "Yes, I have two. The matron of the asylum* made them for me. They're fearfully skimpy. There is never enough to go around in an asylum, so things are always skimpy — at least in a poor asylum like ours. I hate skimpy night-dresses. But one can dream just as well in them as in lovely trailing ones, with frills around the neck, that's one consolation."

"Well, undress as quick as you can and go to bed. I'll come back in a few minutes for the candle. I daren't trust you to put it out yourself. You'd likely set the place on fire."

When Marilla had gone Anne looked around her wistfully. The whitewashed walls were so painfully bare and staring that she thought they must ache over their own bareness... With a sob she hastily discarded her garments, put on the skimpy nightgown and sprang into bed where she burrowed face downward into the pillow and pulled the clothes over her head.

*orphanage

Answer these questions about the extract above.

1 Why is Anne's nightgown skimpy?

....

2 Why does Marilla say she'll come back for the candle later?

....

3 How does Anne feel after Marilla leaves? How can you tell?

....

....

4 How does the language in the extract show that it is from an old novel?

....

....

....

A Modern Text

There were hardly any people on the platform to begin with. Ivo could hear the distant rumble of trains, like monsters in the deep, and for a moment it felt as if he might be one of the only people in this strange underground city, but more filtered through — tourists with cameras slung around their necks, a raucous rugby team on their way to a match, a row of tiny red-capped children in pairs being marshalled by some stressed adults.

Somebody bumped into him and then gripped him by the shoulders. Fear clutched at Ivo. It was a man, tall and thin, young, with crazed, shining eyes. His black hair was plastered to his forehead, his cheeks were reddened; a fat vein throbbed conspicuously in his forehead. The man was panting heavily. Ivo was so shocked he could not speak. Then the man leaned into him. Ivo could smell sweat and a powerful sense of dirt. He noticed that the man's clothes were torn, and he saw what looked like a knife wound in his shoulder, barely cleaned up. Ivo stood frozen, a sick taste rising in his throat. The strange apparition said, in a clear, but low whisper, something that Ivo did not understand, that sounded like 'Remember: Kop-tay thurson', and then grabbed Ivo's hand and thrust something into it.

"Keep it safe. Keep it hidden. They have found me. Remember: *Koptay thurson*. There is no more time. I am Blackwood. They are coming."

Answer these questions about the extract above.

1. Where do you think this extract is set? Explain why you think this.

   ....

   ....

2. What kind of atmosphere does the author create in the extract?

   threatening ☐   carefree ☐   excited ☐   depressed ☐

   How does he create this atmosphere?

   ....

   ....

3. How can you tell from the extract that it is from a modern novel?

   ....

   ....

   ....

Comparing Texts

Sometimes you need to compare two different texts.

Reread the extracts on pages 28 and 29, then answer these questions.

1 Write two words to describe Anne, and two words to describe Blackwood.

Anne is ☐ and ☐

Blackwood is ☐ and ☐

2 Explain how the authors show what the characters are like.

L.M. Montgomery shows this by ....
....

Philip Womack shows this by ....
....

3 Tick all of the techniques that are used in the extract on page 28.

Simile ☐   Metaphor ☐   Personification ☐

> Personification means describing something that isn't human as if it is.

4 Tick all of the techniques that are used in the extract on page 29.

Simile ☐   Metaphor ☐   Personification ☐

Explain which extract you enjoyed reading the most, and why.

....
....
....
....
....
....

Reading Dialects

A dialect is a type of language that's used in a particular region. It uses words and phrases that aren't part of standard English.

Match the dialect words with what you think they mean. Use the internet to help you if you get stuck.

beck   grumpy   barney   stream   grockle

tourist   owt   anything   mardy   argument

Read this extract and then answer the questions.

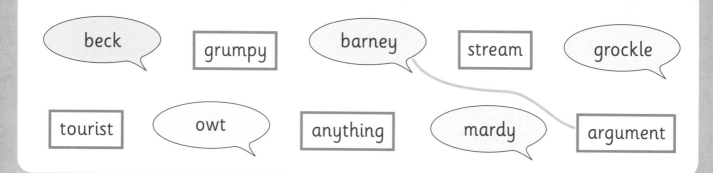

You don't know about me without you have read a book by the name of 'The Adventures of Tom Sawyer'; but that ain't no matter. That book was made by Mr. Mark Twain, and he told the truth, mainly. There was things which he stretched, but mainly he told the truth. That is nothing. I never seen anybody but lied one time or another, without it was Aunt Polly, or the widow, or maybe Mary. Aunt Polly — Tom's Aunt Polly, she is — and Mary, and the Widow Douglas, is all told about in that book, which is mostly a true book; with some stretchers, as I said before.

From 'The Adventures of Huckleberry Finn', by Mark Twain

1   Can you work out what these words from the extract mean?

stretchers ┤   │   │   without it was ┤   │   │

2   Rewrite "there was things which he stretched" in standard English.

....

3   Why do you think Mark Twain used dialect in his book?

....

....

31

Book Reviews

You write book reviews to say what you think of books you've read.

Write a book review of a fiction book you've read.
Use examples from the book to back up your answers.

Title: ....

Author: ....

Plot: ....

....

....

Who was your favourite character? ....

How did this character develop through the book? ....

....

....

....

What did you like about the author's style?

....

....

....

....

Draw your own cover for the book here.

Write two sentences persuading a friend to read it.

....

....

....

....

EP6Q21